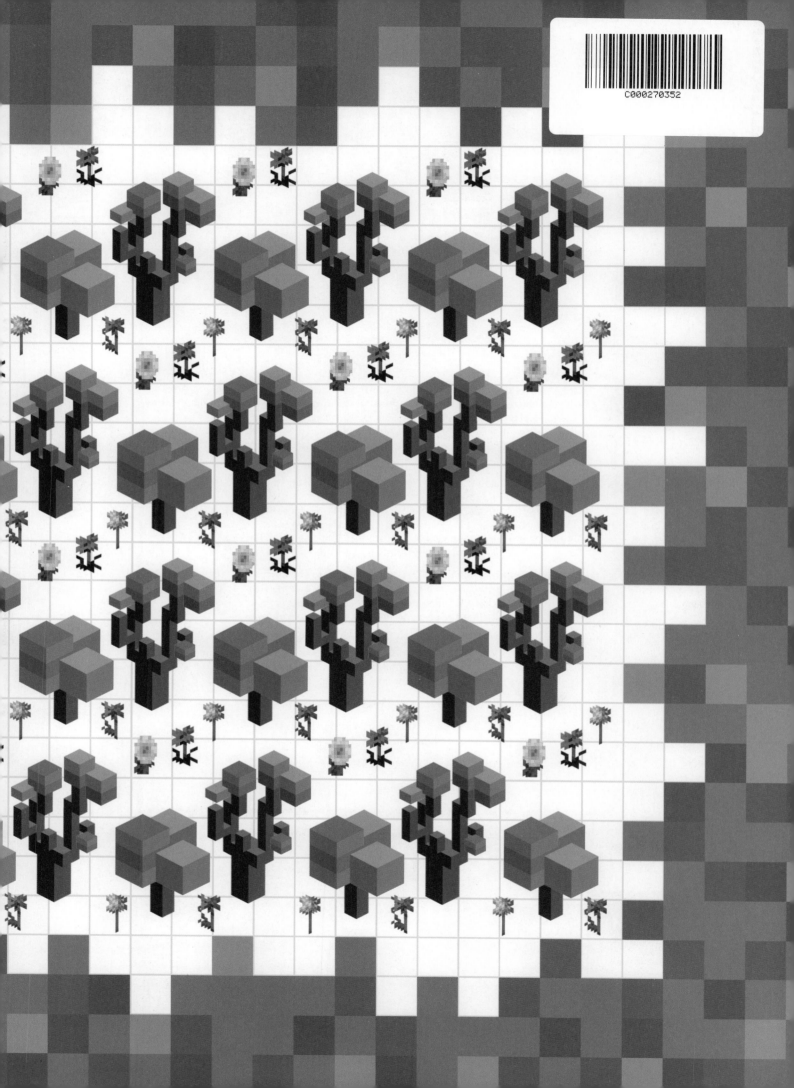

100% Unofficial Minecrafters Unite:

A CENTUM BOOK 978 -1-913865-71-9
Published in Great Britain by Centum Books Ltd
This edition published 2021
1 3 5 7 9 10 8 6 4 2

Text and design © Centum Books | Images © Shutterstock & © Istock

Produced by The Wonderful Ideas Project LTD
with Fiona Munro (Words) and Lisa Robb (Art).
Special consultants: Bobby Chance, Will Shepherd, Jamie & Harry Dockray
Additional illustrations: Caroline Martin

Centum Books Ltd, 20 Devon Square,
Newton Abbot, Devon, TQ12 2HR, UK
9/10 Fenian St, Dublin 2, D02 RX24, Ireland
books@centumbooksltd.co.uk

CENTUM BOOKS Limited Reg. No 07641486

A CIP catalogue record for this book is
available from the British Library.

Printed in China

100% UNOFFICIAL

MINECRAFTERS UNITE

THIS BOOK BELONGS TO

centum

CONTENTS

8-9 >> WELCOME TO ME!

10-11 >> SHOW OFF YOUR SHELTER!

12-13 >> PASSIVE CREATURES

14-15 > RUN AROUND THE BLOCK

16 >>> WHICH TOOL?

17 >>> WHAT'S DIFFERENT?

18-19 > ADVENTURER'S JOURNAL

20-21 > TOOL TRIALS

22-23 > MINING MYSTERY

24 >>> LOST AND FOUND

25 >>> WHAT'S THE RECIPE?

26-27 > ORE-SOME QUIZ!

28-30 > TESTING TIMES

31 >>> WARNING: BIG BOSS

32-33 > NEW ROOMS!

34 >>> PATTERN POWER

35 >>> MIXED UP MUSHROOMS

36-37 > HOSTILE CREATURES

38 >>> MINING - WHAT TO PACK

39 >>> TOP THREE

40-41 > CRAFTING TIPS

42-43 > CREEPER COLOUR

44 >>> POWERFUL POTIONS

45 >>> CROSS BLOCK

46-47 > DEEPER AND DEEPER

48 >>> BLOCK GOALS!

49-50 > MIXED-UP VILLAGERS

51 >>> GUESSING GAME

52-53 > CRAFTING RECIPE IRL

54 >>> STOCK CHECK

55 >>> FIRST DAY, FIRST NIGHT

56-57 > MASTER BUILDERS

58-59 > STAY SAFE HACKS

60 >>> LAUGH YOUR BLOCKS OFF

61 >>> GRID GAME

62-63 > TRUE OR FALSE?

64-65 > JOURNEY TO THE END

66 >>> ORE SEARCH

67 >>> THE BEST BLOCK

68 >>> INSIDE STORY

69 >>> CREATURE FEATURE

70-71 > ALL ABOUT BIOMES

72-73 > MONSTER MASH-UP

74-76 > ANSWERS

77-78 > POSTERS

79 >>> TOP TEN TIPS

WELCOME TO ME!

Use this blank template to create your character's look.

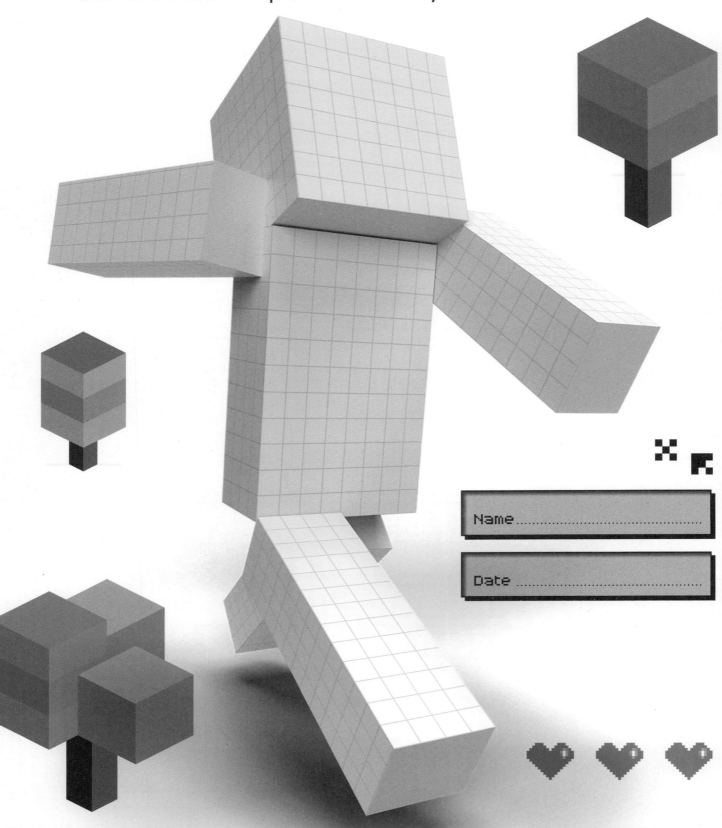

Name ....

Date ....

FAVOURITE HAIR COLOUR

....

....

FAVOURITE HAIRSTYLE

....

....

FAVOURITE JACKET

....

....

FAVOURITE TEE SHIRT

....

....

FAVOURITE TROUSERS

....

....

FAVOURITE FOOTWEAR

....

....

BOOM

LOOT AND TREASURE GUIDE

SHIPWRECKS

THERE ARE THREE TYPES OF CHEST IN A SHIPWRECK:

MAP CHESTS contain paper, feathers, books, buried treasure maps, empty maps, compasses and clocks.

SUPPLY CHESTS contain wheat, rotten flesh, paper, carrot, coal, potato, poisonous potato, gunpowder, pumpkin, enchanted leather clothes (all pieces) and TNT.

TREASURE CHESTS contain iron nuggets, iron ingots, lapis lazuli, emeralds,

SHOW OFF YOUR SHELTER!

Do you ever get stuck for shelter ideas?
You could just have a house of course, but take a look at
the suggestions below for some inspiration for other builds.
Use the grid opposite to plan it and work out what you need.

A mountain hideout

A floating house

A hill fort

A treehouse

An underground lair

A castle

An underwater base

YOU MAY WANT YOUR HOME TO HAVE:

STORAGE SPACE

AN ENTRANCE TO YOUR MINE

ROOM FOR YOUR BED

A CRAFTING AREA

A SMELTING AREA

A FARM FOR FOOD

SPACE TO BREW POTIONS

AN ENCHANTING AREA

HOME SWEET HOME

DID YOU KNOW?
PASSIVE CREATURES

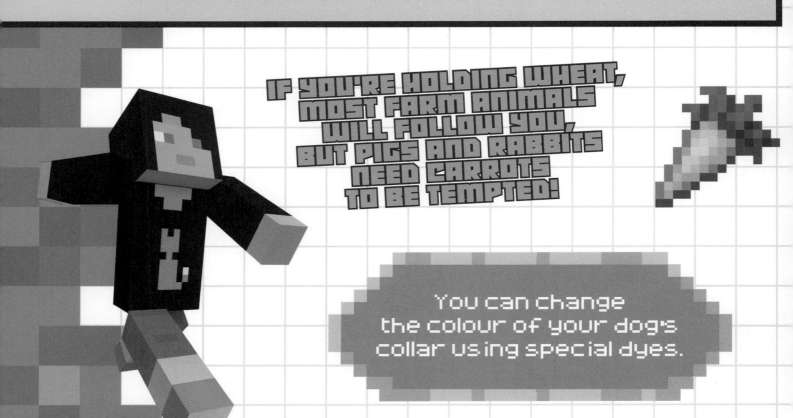

IF YOU'RE HOLDING WHEAT, MOST FARM ANIMALS WILL FOLLOW YOU, BUT PIGS AND RABBITS NEED CARROTS TO BE TEMPTED!

You can change the colour of your dog's collar using special dyes.

BATS, CHICKENS AND COWS CAN BE KEPT AS PETS TOO!

You can easily tame a wolf with bones to become your pet dog, BUT if you want a cat, you need to feed an ocelot some fish - and this is much harder as they are so shy.

You can make friends with a pig, then craft a carrot on a stick to control it while you ride it around. Yee-hah!

HORSES CAN BE PROTECTED FROM MOBS BY CRAFTING SPECIAL ARMOUR.

RUN AROUND THE BLOCK

It's great to be a speedy gamer, but what about running for real? Take this challenge to check your pace.

YOU WILL NEED:

A space big enough to run around, either inside or outside.

WHAT TO DO:

Make a square using coats, sticks or anything else you can find to mark the corners.
Each side should be at least 15 strides long.

Choose one corner to be the start.

1 Run forwards to the first corner and STOP.

2 Side step to the next corner and STOP.

3 Hop towards the next corner and STOP.

4 Run forwards to where you started.

14

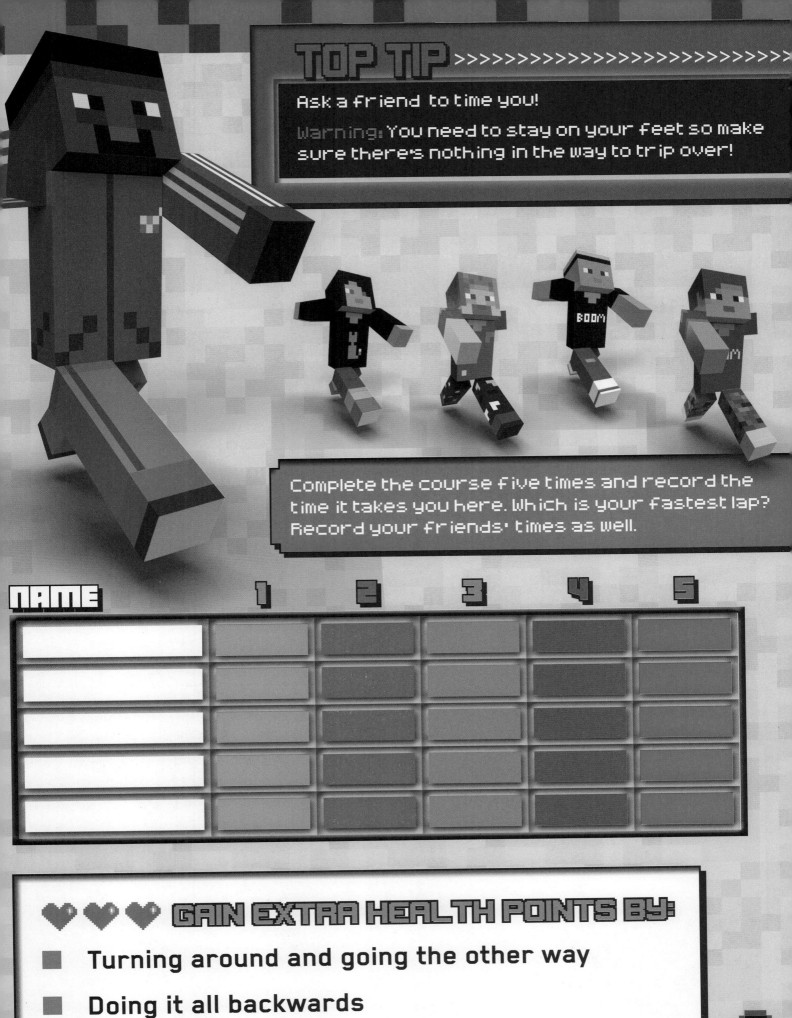

Ask a friend to time you!

Warning: You need to stay on your feet so make sure there's nothing in the way to trip over!

Complete the course five times and record the time it takes you here. Which is your fastest lap? Record your friends' times as well.

NAME	1	2	3	4	5

♥ ♥ ♥ GAIN EXTRA HEALTH POINTS BY:

- Turning around and going the other way

- Doing it all backwards

- Making the square larger

WHICH TOOL?

Work out which tool would be best for each of these jobs. Now draw it in the box.

MINING ORES

TURNING GRASS BLOCKS INTO FARMLAND

COLLECTING WOOD

DIGGING SAND AND DIRT

QUICK QUIZ >>>>>>>>

There is only ONE tool that can be used for mining obsidian. What is it?

Shovel

Hoe

Pickaxe

Axe

Diamond pickaxe

WHAT'S DIFFERENT?

Can you spot and circle 10 differences between these two fishy pictures?

ADVENTURER'S JOURNAL

Imagine you are on a crazy-scary adventure digging deeper and deeper. Fill in the gaps to complete this terrifying tale.

It was dark when we left our home in the

.... biome. My friend,

.... had filled a ....

full of .... and we set off into

the night. I was trembling with fear, would

we meet a .... or a

.... ? We made our way through

the forest. At last we came to the cave entrance

and began to go deeper. At the bottom we

grabbed a .... and began to dig.

I quickly found a .... and a big

....

Just then I thought I heard a sound. Could

it be a .... or maybe even

a .... ? I reached for my

.... and took a deep breath. Would

my .... and my ....

be enough to protect us? I turned and saw a

.... and a ....

It was terrifying. How would we escape and how

would we make our way home?

TOOL TRIALS

Good tools are a necessity when adventuring. You need really good ones, and you need the right one for the job! Design your own below.

MY MINING TOOL IS CALLED A

. . . .

TIPS >>>>>>>>>>>>>>>>>>>>>>>>>>>

Make sure it's really strong.

Does it have different heads?

What ore is it made from?

MY FARMING TOOL IS CALLED A

. . . .

TIPS >>>>>>>>>>>>>>>>>>>>>>>>>>>>

Is it for harvesting or planting?

Is it for feeding animals?

What colour is it?

MY LIGHT TOOL IS CALLED A

. . . .

TIPS >>>>>>>>>>>>>>>>>>>>>>>>>

Would it be hand-held or more of
a lamp or lantern?

How is it powered?

What is it made of?

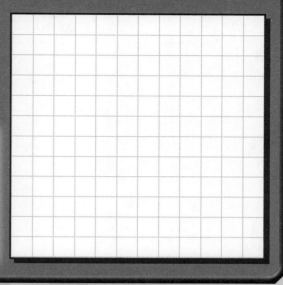

MY WEAPON IS CALLED A

. . . .

TIPS >>>>>>>>>>>>>>>>>>>>>>>>>>>

Is your weapon like a sword?

Or like a bow and arrow?

Does it need ammunition?

DID YOU KNOW? >>>>>>>>>>>>>>>>>>>>>>>>>>

Swords in Minecraft can be made from different
materials. Netherite is the strongest, then diamond,
iron, stone, gold and wooden planks.

MINING MYSTERY

Dig deep and find all the words in this massive grid.

Word List:
- ORE
- DIAMOND
- EMERALD
- PICKAXE
- TRIDENT
- CAVE
- TORCH
- GRAVEL
- LAVA
- REDSTONE
- BEDROCK
- GOLD
- LAPIS
- SHOVEL
- CHEST
- LADDER
- BUCKET
- FOOD
- WOOD
- SWORD
- BOW
- ARROWS
- NETHER

E	X	A	K	C	I	P	E	J	Q	Z	E
P	R	H	J	O	W	C	M	R	H	V	U
U	A	T	R	O	N	B	E	B	A	J	I
P	P	L	A	G	R	I	R	C	S	V	O
D	I	A	M	O	N	D	A	E	U	O	I
R	E	H	T	E	N	K	L	O	R	V	R
C	T	Y	I	E	D	E	D	T	Y	G	L
K	A	Q	Y	B	L	U	H	G	C	D	H
R	C	B	F	S	N	T	J	Q	D	R	L
P	K	O	I	M	H	P	B	F	T	A	X
T	Q	I	R	V	N	V	Z	A	L	B	F
P	F	D	R	D	A	X	Z	S	A	Q	S
B	A	B	J	T	E	W	Z	R	S	F	G
R	V	B	P	Z	X	B	R	O	E	D	Y
Q	W	X	G	X	K	O	D	K	W	J	Q
V	Q	B	W	F	W	K	S	O	K	V	W
W	O	O	D	S	N	O	M	S	O	N	P
Z	W	W	Y	J	L	B	V	L	M	X	K

Answers on PAGE 74

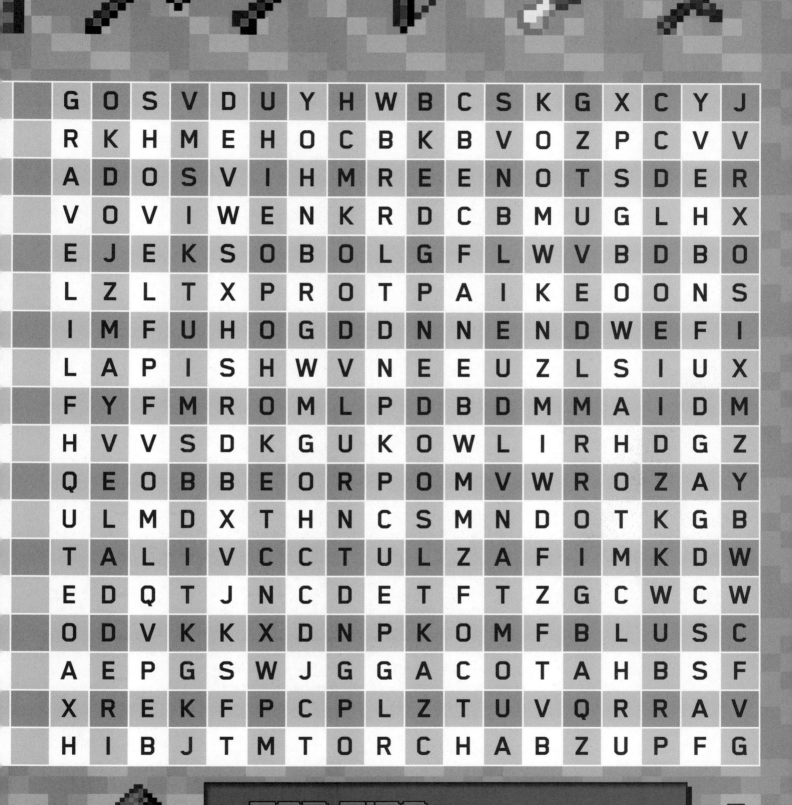

G	O	S	V	D	U	Y	H	W	B	C	S	K	G	X	C	Y	J
R	K	H	M	E	H	O	C	B	K	B	V	O	Z	P	C	V	V
A	D	O	S	V	I	H	M	R	E	E	N	O	T	S	D	E	R
V	O	V	I	W	E	N	K	R	D	C	B	M	U	G	L	H	X
E	J	E	K	S	O	B	O	L	G	F	L	W	V	B	D	B	O
L	Z	L	T	X	P	R	O	T	P	A	I	K	E	O	O	N	S
I	M	F	U	H	O	G	D	D	N	N	E	N	D	W	E	F	I
L	A	P	I	S	H	W	V	N	E	E	U	Z	L	S	I	U	X
F	Y	F	M	R	O	M	L	P	D	B	D	M	M	A	I	D	M
H	V	V	S	D	K	G	U	K	O	W	L	I	R	H	D	G	Z
Q	E	O	B	B	E	O	R	P	O	M	V	W	R	O	Z	A	Y
U	L	M	D	X	T	H	N	C	S	M	N	D	O	T	K	G	B
T	A	L	I	V	C	C	T	U	L	Z	A	F	I	M	K	D	W
E	D	Q	T	J	N	C	D	E	T	F	T	Z	G	C	W	C	W
O	D	V	K	K	X	D	N	P	K	O	M	F	B	L	U	S	C
A	E	P	G	S	W	J	G	G	A	C	O	T	A	H	B	S	F
X	R	E	K	F	P	C	P	L	Z	T	U	V	Q	R	R	A	V
H	I	B	J	T	M	T	O	R	C	H	A	B	Z	U	P	F	G

TOP TIPS >>>>>>>>>>>>>>>>>>>

Search left, right, up, down, diagonally, forwards and backwards.

No words are split across both pages.

LOST AND FOUND

Help this baby rabbit find a way out through the maze to join the rest of his family.

START

FINISH

It's hungry work so help him pick up four carrots on the way. Chomp! Chomp!

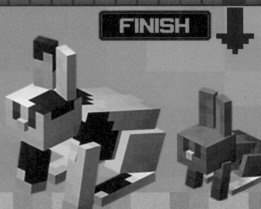

Answers on PAGE 74

WHAT'S THE RECIPE?

Work out what you need to make these three things.
Find what you need and copy them into the right crafting table.

Diamond Axe

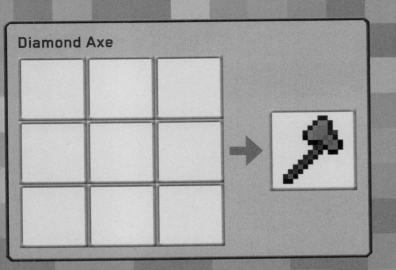

TOP TIPS >>>>>>>>>>>>

To use a bow, you must have arrows in your inventory.

Remember to draw the right number of each item!

Compass

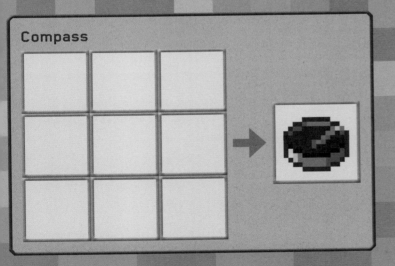

Bow

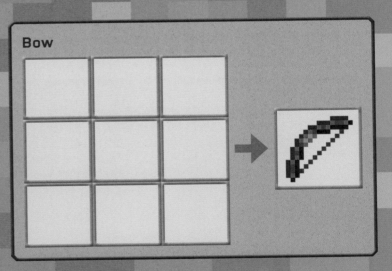

| Iron ingots | Iron ingots | Redstone dust | Diamonds | Sticks | Sticks | Sticks | Strings |
| Iron ingots | Iron ingots | Diamonds | Diamonds | Sticks | Sticks | Strings | Strings |

ORE-SOME QUIZ!

Test your deep, deep knowledge of the underground adventuring worlds.

1 What should you take with you to store valuables?

a   An ore bath
b   An ender chest
c   A block bag

2 Which of these is NOT a type of mining?

a   Cave mining
b   Strip mining
c   Over mining

3 Caves are typically found below what layer?

a   54
b   3
c   10

4 Which of these cannot naturally spawn underground?

a   Skeleton
b   Cow
c   Spider

5 Which of these ores is the most rare?

a   Redstone
b   Lapis lazuli
c   Emerald

6 Whilst exploring a cavern, you are poisoned by a cave spider. What do you need to help you?

- a Carrots
- b Rotten flesh
- c Bucket of milk

7 Which ore is found at the deepest level?

- a Iron
- b Diamond
- c Gold

8 Which ore can only be mined with a diamond pickaxe?

- a Obsidian
- b Emerald
- c Quartz

9 Which block is deepest underground?

- a Cobblestone
- b Bedrock
- c Granite

10 Glowstone spawns naturally in only which place?

- a Basalt Deltas
- b Plains
- c The Nether

Answers on PAGE 74

TESTING TIMES

Become better at the game by setting challenges to help you improve. Try and complete each challenge card and log your results below.

Ask an adult to cut out the cards along the dotted lines, shuffle the deck and randomly pick a challenge to attempt!

BLOCK 'N' ROLL 💀

	Difficulty rating	Time taken	Attempts made
1			
2			
3			
4			
5			
6			
7			
8			
9			

STAY SAFE TIP >>>>>>>>>>>>>>>>>>>>>>>>>>>>

Mine carefully to avoid falling sand and gravel, and watch out for flowing lava when digging upwards.

MASTER BUILDER

Build a replica of your own home

PARTY TIME!

Make a cake

ROYAL COMMAND

Design a castle, with a moat and drawbridge

FRIEND ZONE

Get three pets

LOADS OF LAYERS

Make a house that has five floors

'SHROOM SEARCH

Find a mushroom biome

JEWEL DUEL

Be the first to mine a diamond on multiplayer mode

PROTECTION SECTION

Get a full set of every type of armour

END GAME

Defeat the Ender Dragon

 LOOT AND TREASURE GUIDE

MINE FOR DIAMONDS AT Y-LEVEL 11.

That's deep enough for diamonds, but not so deep you risk mining into a lava pool.

CHALLENGE CARD

100% UNOFFICIAL

MINECRAFTERS UNITE

CHALLENGE CARD

100% UNOFFICIAL

MINECRAFTERS UNITE

CHALLENGE CARD

100% UNOFFICIAL

MINECRAFTERS UNITE

CHALLENGE CARD

100% UNOFFICIAL

MINECRAFTERS UNITE

CHALLENGE CARD

100% UNOFFICIAL

MINECRAFTERS UNITE

CHALLENGE CARD

100% UNOFFICIAL

MINECRAFTERS UNITE

CHALLENGE CARD

100% UNOFFICIAL

MINECRAFTERS UNITE

CHALLENGE CARD

100% UNOFFICIAL

MINECRAFTERS UNITE

CHALLENGE CARD

100% UNOFFICIAL

MINECRAFTERS UNITE

DID YOU KNOW?

30

Gold is one of the rarest ores, but it creates the weakest tools.

WARNING: BIG BOSS

The Ender Dragon is a dangerous flying hostile Boss Mob.
Enormous wings make her difficult to take on and defeat.
She can pass through all blocks, and destroy almost all of them.
This creepy creature will target, dive down and attack players.

Some equipment you will need to take her on:

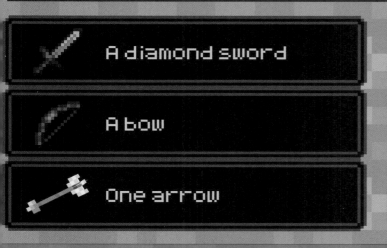

A diamond sword

A bow

One arrow

A diamond pickaxe

Ten golden apples

Six healing potions

NEW ROOMS!

What would be in your dream home? You may not have it in real life, but you can create it in your Minecraft world! Get creative and draw four special spaces here. There are some ideas below.

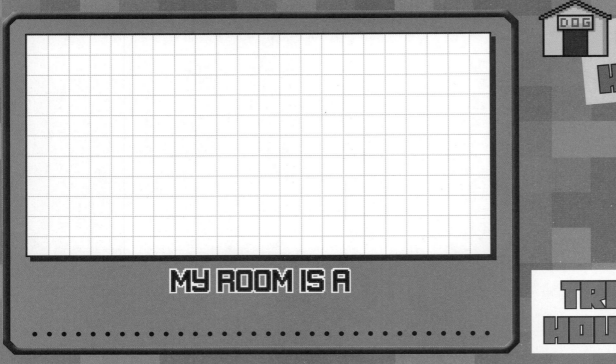

MY ROOM IS A

. . . .

DOG HOUSE

TREE HOUSE

ICE CREAM PARLOUR

TENNIS COURT

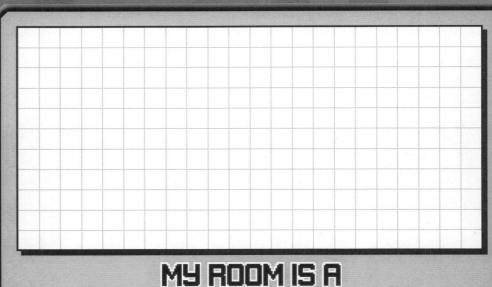

MY ROOM IS A

. . . .

PLAYROOM

GAMING DEN

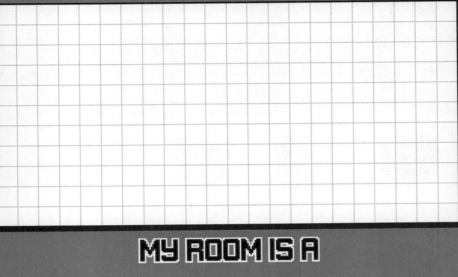

MY ROOM IS A

PIZZA PARLOUR

POOL HOUSE

FOOTBALL PITCH

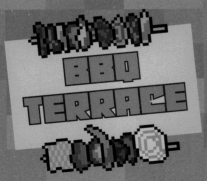

BBQ TERRACE

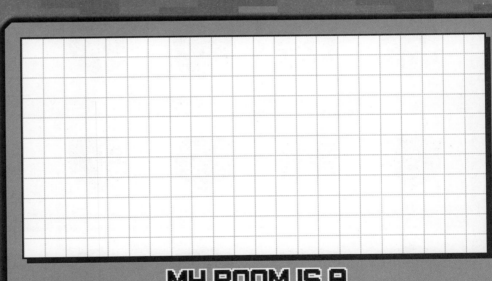

MY ROOM IS A

When you are totally happy with your design, create it online!

PATTERN POWER

Complete the colour sequences below by working out which block comes next. Colour in the blocks with the right colours.

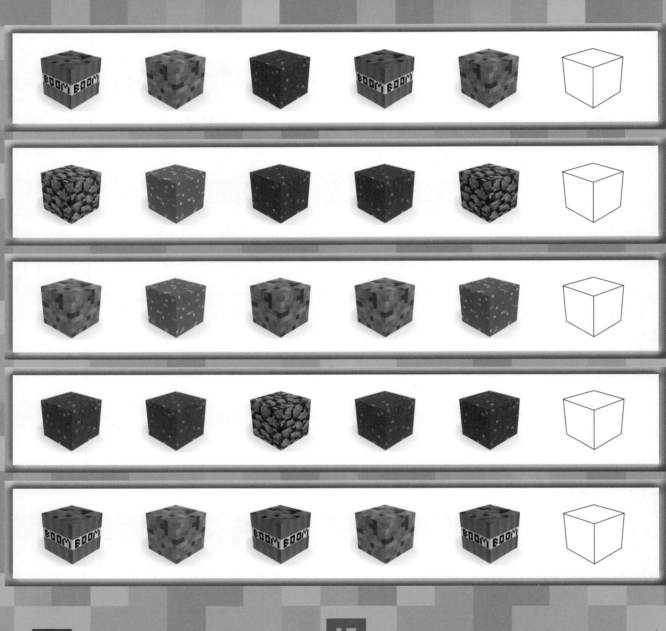

Answers on PAGE 74

MIXED UP MUSHROOMS

If you think all these mushrooms are the same, look again! There is ONE that is different to all the others. Circle it if you can find it!

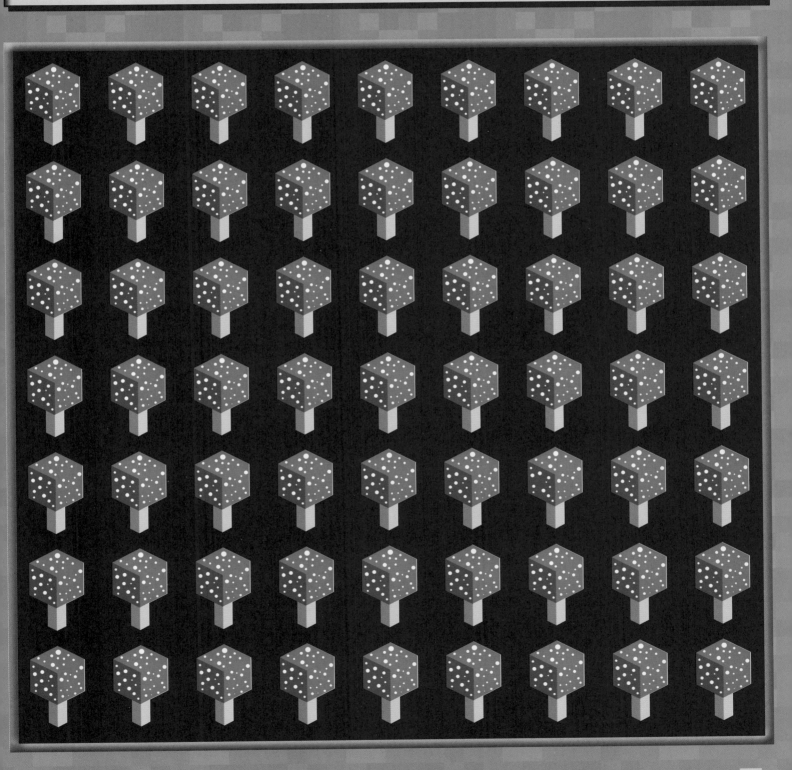

Answers on PAGE 74

DID YOU KNOW?
HOSTILE CREATURES

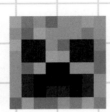

Skeletons sink in water. They cannot swim ... but be warned. They do not drown.

A CREEPER COULD NEVER HURT A CAT - THEY ARE SCARED OF THEM.

Guardians are hostile fish that will always spawn in or around ocean monuments.

YUK FACT: IF YOU KILL A SLIME IT WILL JUST MULTIPLY AND YOU'LL BE IN EVEN MORE TROUBLE!

If you manage to tame a spider, you'll need a saddle to ride it!

SLIMES SPAWN MOSTLY DURING A FULL MOON.

MINING - WHAT TO PACK

You need to get packed up for a mining adventure!
Tick the eight most useful items.

☐ compass	☐ arrow	☐ egg	☐ crafting table
☐ flowers	☐ potion	☐ pickaxe	☐ potato
☐ fruit	☐ torch	☐ flower pot	☐ bow
☐ boat	☐ blocks	☐ cooked food	☐ sword

Now put a cross against the four LEAST useful!

TOP THREE

There is so much to do in Minecraft.
Write down your top three in the categories below:

TOOLS:

WEAPONS:

PETS:

ORES TO MINE:

BIOMES TO LIVE IN:

MATES TO GAME WITH:

CRAFTING TIPS

It can be dangerous out there so it's important to make sure you're prepared. When you are out and about, always take a bed. If you lose track of time you can get some rest – and be safe.

READY FOR BREAD?

Once you have tamed some wolves, sow leftover bonemeal on grass blocks to start a wheat farm. 6-8 doses can create enough wheat for a loaf of bread. Useful for emergencies.

LIGHT WORK

Make a lava bucket. This will be excellent for killing large numbers of mobs in one go and lighting up the area at the same time.

ON THE EDGE

Make sure you crouch when you are on a cliff. This will prevent you from accidentally walking off the edge.

SAFE BASE

Build your base above ground for safety. Craft a ladder to get in and out.

WOOD WORKS

When you collect wood blocks, collect a lot. You will use them for many things.

SEEING THE LIGHT

NEVER run out of torches.

SHEEP TIP

Don't kill sheep for their wool. You will get more if you shear them.

SPACE RACE

When you are out, don't clutter your inventory with items you won't need. This leaves space for items you might find.

HOT STUFF!

When smelting, always try to add items to the furnace in multiples of eight to avoid wasting fuel.

CREEPER COLOUR

Draw your own Creeper square by square.
Grab every green you have to colour it in then . . . run!

POWERFUL POTIONS

Test your maths super skills here! Work out which number each of these potions represents by working backwards from the answers given.

Tip: No potion bottle has a value more than 10

🧪 + 🧪 + 🧪 = 18

🧪 + 🧪 + 🧪 = 14

🧪 + 🧪 + 🧪 = 17

🧪 − 🧪 = 1

🧪 = ☐   🧪 = ☐   🧪 = ☐

44

Answers on PAGE 75

CROSS BLOCK

Test your Minecraft knowledge with this crossword.

ACROSS

2. The Minecraft world is made of these.
5. An alternate dimension of the Minecraft world.
7. One of the most versatile raw materials in the game.
9. Regions in Minecraft.

DOWN

1. The most common ore in the game.
3. An aggressive mob.
4. An aggressive flying mob.
6. Type of video game with an 'open world' design.
8. The creators of Minecraft.
10. The basic male default skin in the game.

Fancy a challenge? Set yourself a five-minute timer.

DEEPER AND DEEPER

How will you make your way to the bottom of this huge cave? Be careful as you dig your way through – just in case there are creatures around corners.

START

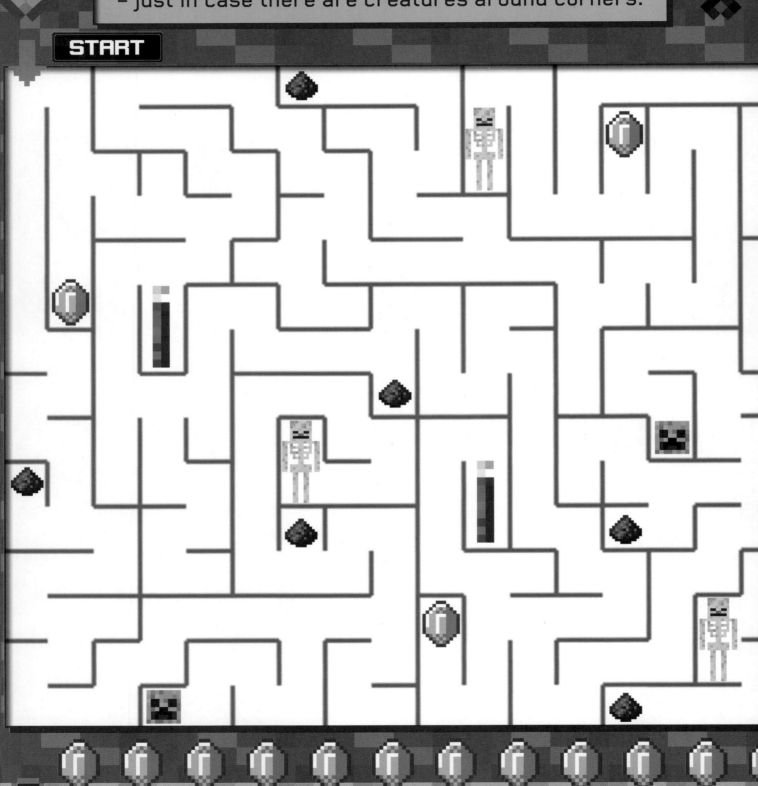

Answers on PAGE 75

Pick up three emeralds and two torches along the way!

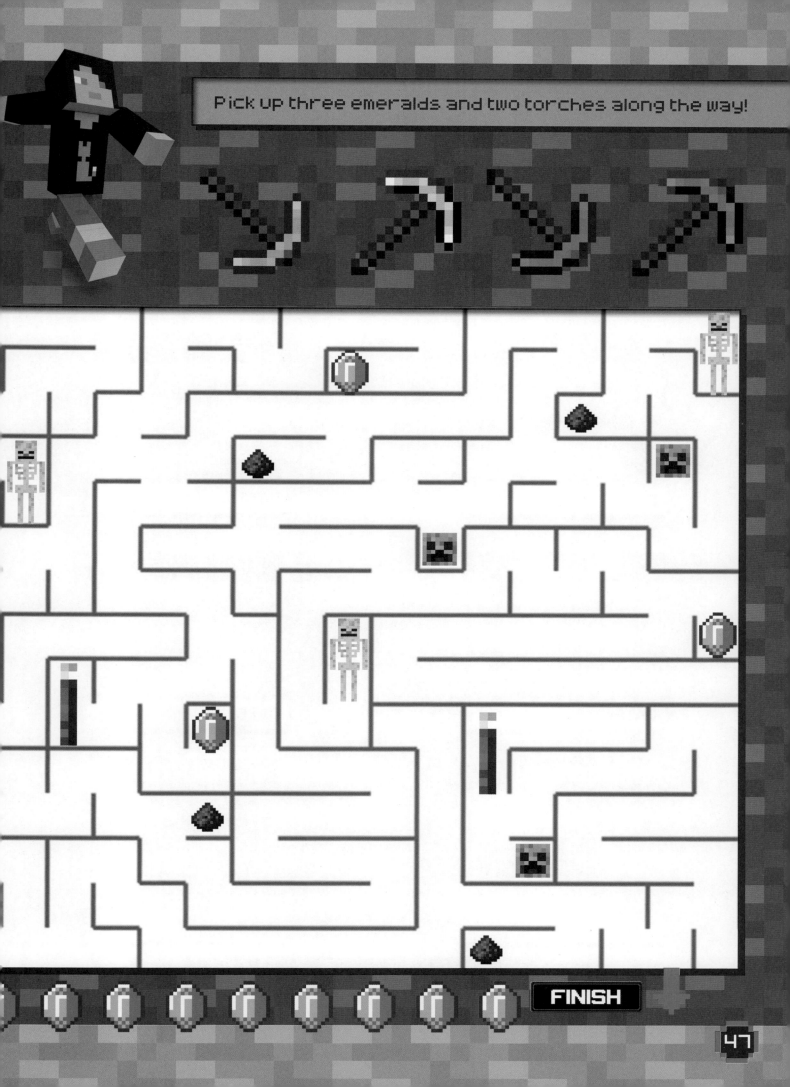

FINISH

BLOCK GOALS!

Want to build something from a film in creative mode?
Maybe you want to fight a dragon, or just have as much fun
as possible? Write down your goals below so you don't forget.

Build Goal

....

....

DATE:

Creative Goal

....

....

DATE:

Survival Goal

....

....

DATE:

Exploration Goal

....

....

DATE:

Fun Goal

....

....

DATE:

Ultimate Goal

....

....

DATE:

Write the date under each
goal as you complete it.

MIXED-UP VILLAGERS

Ask an adult to cut out the villagers carefully along the dotted lines shown. Now turn them over and, following the guides, cut each one into three pieces (ouch!). Now shuffle the pieces, lay them out, and turn one over. Turn the remaining pieces over one at a time until each villager is complete again.

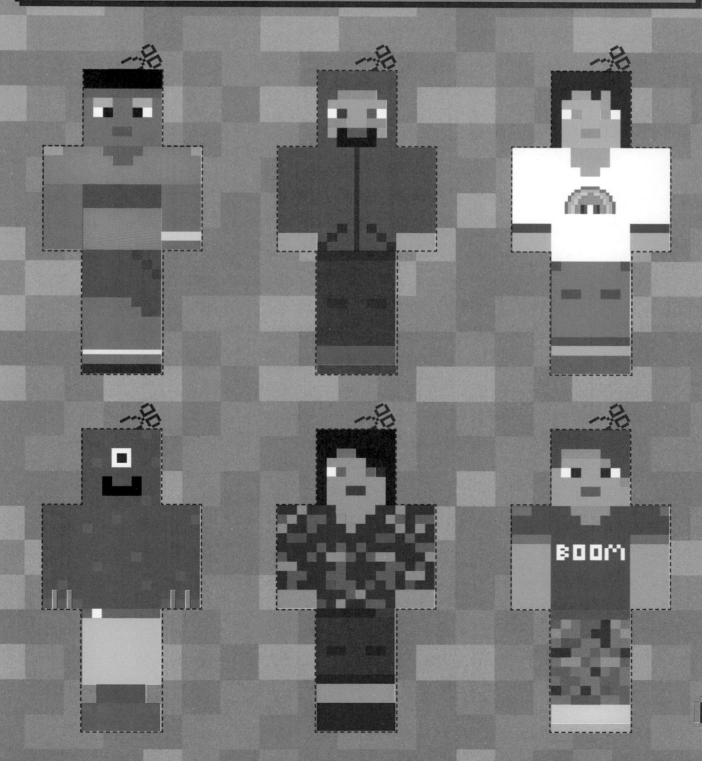

If you turn over a piece you don't need, turn it back over but try to remember where it is. You will need it later on in the game!

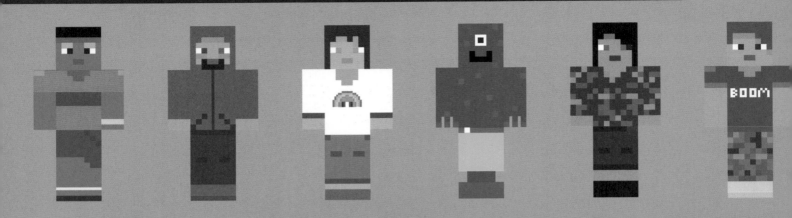

Set a timer and see how quickly you can put your villagers back together again!

GUESSING GAME

Can you tell what part of the Minecraft game is being described by answering just three clues?

1
It is brown.

It can have a green top.

It can change colour depending on what biome it is in.

2
It is a neutral mob.

It has unique teleportation abilities.

It has purple eyes.

3
It is a passive mob.

It can mumble.

It will run inside at night or during rain.

4
It spawns at a light level of 7 or less.

Spiders have a 1% chance to spawn with one of them riding it.

It is hostile.

5
It is a neutral mob.

It is found in the Nether.

It will attack you if you do not have at least one piece of golden armour.

Answers on PAGE 75

CRAFTING RECIPE IRL

Dirt Blocks with Hidden Ores
Make these to share with your friends.
Just what you need after some serious gaming!

INGREDIENTS:

- 190g butter
- 190g dark chocolate
- 3 eggs
- 250g caster sugar
- 115g plain flour
- A handful of coloured sugar-coated chocolate beans

Always check with a
grown up before cooking.

EQUIPMENT:

- Two large mixing bowls
- Large saucepan
- Wooden spoon
- Spatula
- A rectangular baking tin that measures about 34cm x 20cm
- Baking paper

1.
Ask an adult to preheat the oven to 180°C/160° (fan) gas 4.

2.
Line your tin with baking paper. Make sure it reaches over the top of the sides. This will help when you want to lift your Dirt Blocks out of the tin.

3.

Melt the butter and chocolate together over a low heat in the large pan.

4.

In one bowl use the wooden spoon to beat the eggs with the sugar.

5.

Put the flour into the other bowl.

6.

When the chocolate mixture has melted let it cool for a few minutes and stir in the egg and sugar mixture.

7.

Now stir in the flour and beat until the mixture is smooth.

Make sure the mixture is not too hot when you add the chocolate beans or they will melt!

8.

Scrape your mixture into the lined tin and bake for 20 minutes.

9.

When it's ready, the top should be dried and pale brown. The middle should be dark and gooey. While still warm, push a handful of coloured chocolate beans into the top for precious ores!

10.

Cool your Dirt Blocks in the tin and then cut into squares and **EAT!**

STOCK CHECK

Look at the two packed inventories below. They may look the same but if you look really closely you will see that one is slightly different. Circle three differences on the bottom picture.

Answers on PAGE 75

FIRST DAY, FIRST NIGHT

Can you remember your first day playing in survival mode?
It probably went by faster than you can say 'Minecrafters'.
How many of these tasks did you complete?

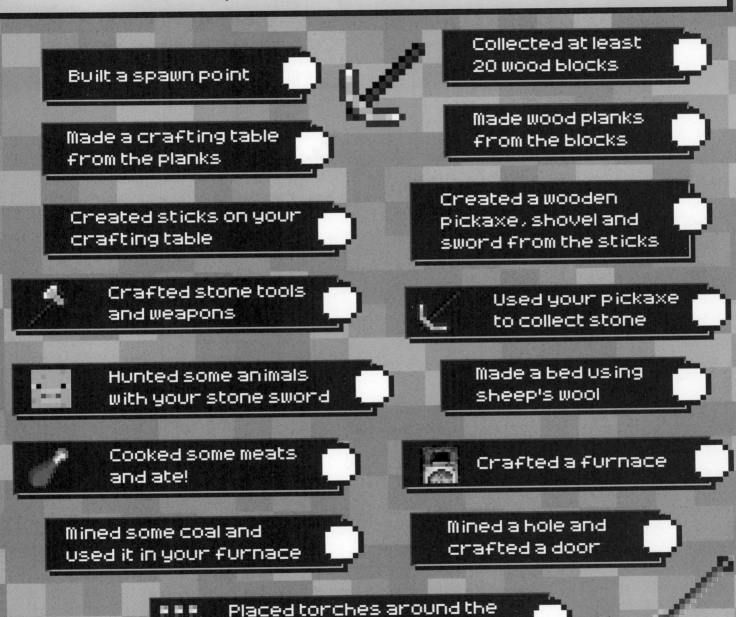

Built a spawn point ⚪

Collected at least 20 wood blocks ⚪

Made a crafting table from the planks ⚪

Made wood planks from the blocks ⚪

Created sticks on your crafting table ⚪

Created a wooden pickaxe, shovel and sword from the sticks ⚪

Crafted stone tools and weapons ⚪

Used your pickaxe to collect stone ⚪

Hunted some animals with your stone sword ⚪

Made a bed using sheep's wool ⚪

Cooked some meats and ate! ⚪

Crafted a furnace ⚪

Mined some coal and used it in your furnace ⚪

Mined a hole and crafted a door ⚪

Placed torches around the shelter to keep nasties away ⚪

HOW MANY DID YOU GET?  ⚪ /15

If you got **10** or more then you're seriously switched-on!

MASTER BUILDERS

There are lots of things to remember when you are constructing. Follow these tips to make sure that your buildings are the best.

IF YOU'VE JUST STARTED, THINK SMALL. DON'T TRY TO BUILD A MANSION WITH A MOAT BEFORE NIGHTFALL!

BUILD WITH OBSIDIAN AS IT CAN'T BE DESTROYED EASILY.

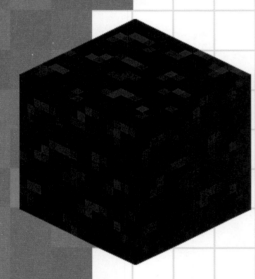

Use a night-activating lava trap to defend your home.

KEEP A CHEST BY YOUR DOOR, SO YOU CAN GATHER UP ESSENTIALS BEFORE HEADING OUT.

Keep your bed in a secure bunker in the centre of your home so a mob cannot prevent you from sleeping or blow up your bed.

FOR EXTRA SECURITY BUILD USING THREE-LAYERED WALLS, WITH THE MIDDLE ONE BEING OBSIDIAN OR WATER.

Make a good plan, maybe on paper, before you start. Planning is everything.

Make use of different textures. A white wall can look special by using bone blocks, white wool and quartz mixed up.

CHOOSE YOUR COLOURS CAREFULLY SO IT ALL BLENDS WELL TOGETHER.

PROVIDE MOOD LIGHTING IN YOUR HOME USING ICE OR WATER BLOCKS.

STAY SAFE HACKS

WATCH OUT FOR ZOMBIE VILLAGES

THERE IS A 2% CHANCE OF ONE SPAWNING.

You'll know you're entering a zombie village by the decor. No torches, lots of cobwebs and no doors are a clue – apart from the zombie villagers of course!

TOP TIP! ♥ ♥ ♥ ♥ ♥ ♥ ♥ ♥ ♥ ♥ ♥ ♥

Keeping your hunger bar full will replenish your health and allow you to run, so always carry food. Cake and rabbit stew restore the most hearts, but cake has low saturation so your hunger will start dropping again soon after eating it, and rabbit stew takes a lot of crafting. Cooked steak and pork chops are the best food sources. They restore 8 points of health and 12.8 points of saturation and they stack in the inventory, so you can carry plenty!

KEEP IT LIGHT ♥ ♥ ♥ ♥ ♥ ♥ ♥ ♥ ♥ ♥ ♥ ♥

Light levels matter – a lot. Light keeps hostile mobs from spawning and draws in friendly mobs, whereas the dark can hide all manner of evil creatures who are just waiting to separate you from your long-term plans. You can never have too many torches, so place them frequently and often. They don't just keep evil mobs away, they're also handy if you want to find your way back from a long journey once night falls!

DON'T GET INTO A FIGHT

Staying out of fights you can't win is key to long-term survival. Skill aside, fights don't become easier the more you win them. The best way to deal with this? Don't get into fights at all. This might sound obvious, but it's easy to be too confident once you've won a few. If you see three creepers in a tight space, the best way to stay alive is to get out of there as quickly as possible.

LISTEN OUT

It's easy to focus on the stuff you can see around you, but don't forget to keep your ears open too, especially when you're underground. Listening to sounds around you is the perfect way to navigate away from danger. A zombie's moan, a skeleton's bony clink or the hiss of a creeper can all tell you danger's around, while bubbling lava or running water let you know there's a cavern – and some potential riches – close by!

DRESS FOR THE OCCASION

Always wear the best armour you can. Once you have an iron pickaxe, get some iron armour. Once you start finding diamonds, save them for diamond armour. You can't die if you can't be hurt, and wearing the strongest possible armour will take care of it. Leather armour is just for decoration – by the time you can even find enough leather to craft it, you should be well on your way to smelting ingots!

ALWAYS LOOK DOWN

Fall damage is the hardest type of damage to protect yourself against, and there's almost no way to guard against it altogether. If you have to make a long drop, aim to land in some water to avoid damage completely, while landing on a bed, hay bale or slime block will also reduce damage. What you should really do is use the sneak key near a ledge, as you can't fall while you're sneaking!

LAUGH YOUR BLOCKS OFF!

Here are some great gags to entertain your friends!

HA HA

MY FRIEND WAS MINING WITH A PICKAXE.
Luckily his injuries were . . . minor.

HOW DO YOU CUT DOWN A TREE IN MINECRAFT?
How WOOD I know?

HOW DO CRAFTERS AVOID SUNBURN?
Sunblock

LOL!

LOL!

WHAT DO YOU GET IF YOU SPAWN A LOT OF KITTENS?
A meowtain!

WHY COULDN'T THE VILLAGER BREAK THE BEDROCK?
It was just too hard.

WHAT'S SO GOOD ABOUT COBBLESTONE?
It's hand-PICKED!

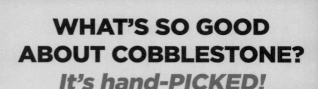

WHAT DID THE VILLAGER SAY WHEN HE GOT BACK FROM THE CAVE?
It was ore-ful!

GRID GAME

Look carefully at the grid below and work out what goes in the missing squares. No item can be repeated in any row or column.

Draw the right item in each square!

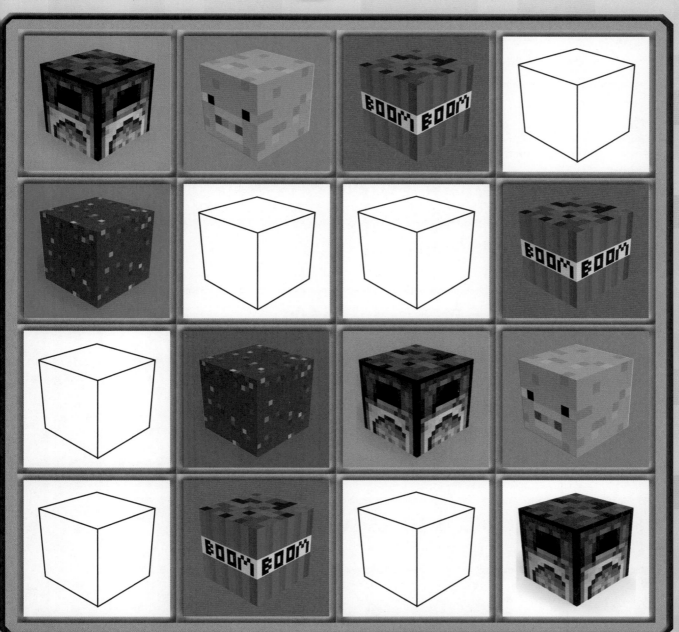

TRUE OR FALSE?

What's right and what's not?
Test your block brain power with this quick quiz!

1. Zombies don't burn in the sun ◯

2. The maximum build height is 159 blocks ◯

3. Mobs cannot spawn on carpet ◯

4. The Ghast mob exists in The End ◯

5. The pufferfish poisons you if eaten ◯

6. You need a portal to enter the Nether ◯

7. Fishing rods can be enchanted ◯

8. Gold tools are stronger than iron tools ◯

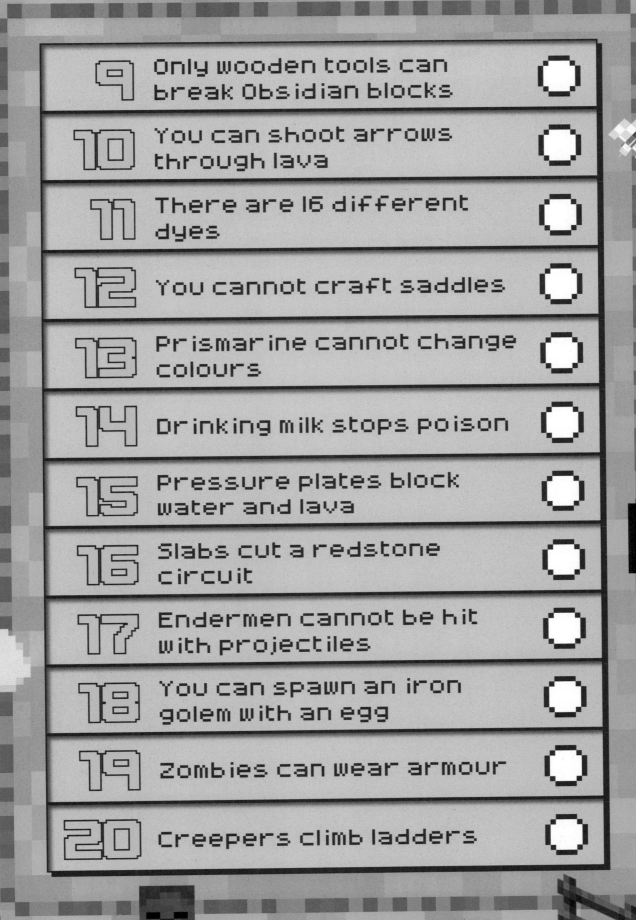

9	Only wooden tools can break Obsidian blocks	○
10	You can shoot arrows through lava	○
11	There are 16 different dyes	○
12	You cannot craft saddles	○
13	Prismarine cannot change colours	○
14	Drinking milk stops poison	○
15	Pressure plates block water and lava	○
16	Slabs cut a redstone circuit	○
17	Endermen cannot be hit with projectiles	○
18	You can spawn an iron golem with an egg	○
19	Zombies can wear armour	○
20	Creepers climb ladders	○

Answers on PAGE 76

JOURNEY TO THE END

Make your way from grassland, through mines to The End and stay away from the baddies.

START

THE END

ORE SEARCH

Can you fit the names of eight different ores into this grid?

The first one has been added to help you.

EMERALD

COPPER

LAPIS

COAL

REDSTONE

IRON

GOLD

EMERALD

DIAMOND

THE BEST BLOCK

Design and make your very own block.
Colour the squares and then ask an adult to carefully cut out the shape.
Now fold where shown.

Look over the page before you start cutting.

Be careful not to cut off the tabs!

That's block-tastic!

INSIDE STORY

This will be the inside of your block. Draw and colour some treasure.

Match the coloured tabs to the coloured edge.

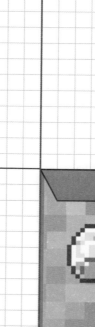

CREATURE FEATURE

We got pigs! We got dolphins! We've even got dragons! Is there an animal or creature that you would love to see in the game? Doodle your top three choices in the pixel grids below.

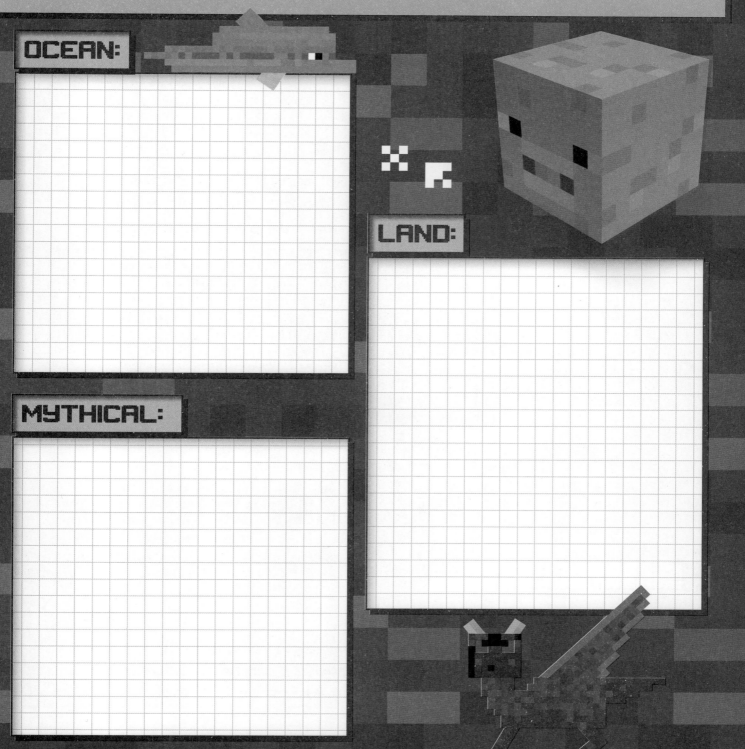

OCEAN:

LAND:

MYTHICAL:

ALL ABOUT BIOMES

There are over 60 biomes to discover in the game. That's a lot! How many have you ventured into? Let's break down the main biomes you can find.

There are five main types of biomes, Lush, Snowy, Cold, Dry and Ocean. Within these are variations and even sub variations. Let's explore a few of them.

LUSH:

PLAINS:

Iconic grass blocks. Low hills. Not many trees or flowers. Watch out for cave openings in the ground. Lava pools are often found here. You'll be able to get yourself a horse, yee-hah!

JUNGLE:

Amazing tall redwood trees grow here, but the vegetation is dense and hard work, as are the hostiles. If you have the stamina they are a great resource for useful items. Cocoa beans to make cookies are a favourite. Also look out for ocelots – you can tame them.

SNOWY:

ICE PLAINS:

Flat and covered in ice and snow – water freezes here instantly! You might be lucky enough to spot a roaming polar bear. Igloos can be found here and most contain loot.

EXTREME HILLS:

Dramatic hills rise up from the ground in this cold biome that can flit between snow and rain. Climb to the top of the hills for amazing views into the distance – just don't fall! You'll love the llamas that spawn here, but not so much the silverfish.

DRY:

DESERT:

Full of sand and cacti and not much else – this is a very hard place to survive. Look out for villages, wells and temples. Some temples can even be found beneath the sand – so keep a look out for clues to lots of lovely loot.

SAVANNAH:

Very dry with no rainfall and lots of flat land. Here you'll find the odd village. Lots of horses and llamas roam the open space too.

OCEAN:

OCEAN AND DEEP OCEAN:

The ocean biomes make up 60% of the game's surface. Get around by swimming or building your very own boat. There is lots of food here and plenty to find and explore, including shipwrecks, temple ruins and buried treasure. Just watch out for hostiles who can pack a real punch, especially if they are armed with a trident.

MONSTER MASH-UP

How good are your spotting skills? Look really closely at the picture and count the correct number of items listed. Tick the boxes as you find them!

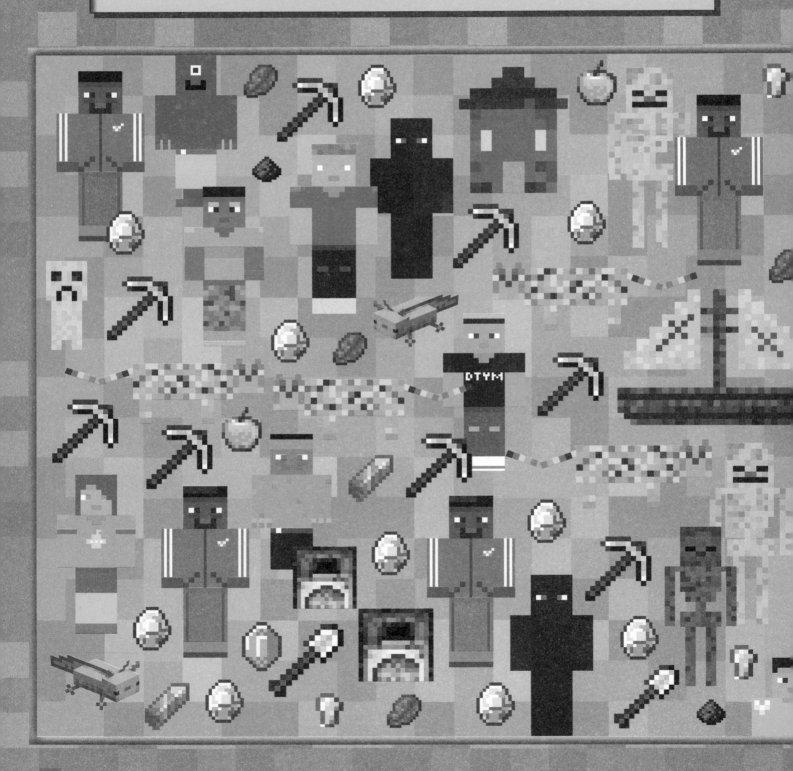

Answers on PAGE 76

6 ocelots

3 axolotls

5 villagers in blue tops

2 villagers in red tops

1 creeper

4 Endermen

2 skeletons

11 pickaxes

3 shovels

15 diamonds

1 emerald

4 furnaces

ANSWERS

PAGE 16:

TURNING GRASS BLOCKS INTO FARMLAND

COLLECTING WOOD

DIGGING SAND AND DIRT

MINING ORES

QUICK QUIZ

PAGE 17:

PAGE 24:

PAGE 22-23:

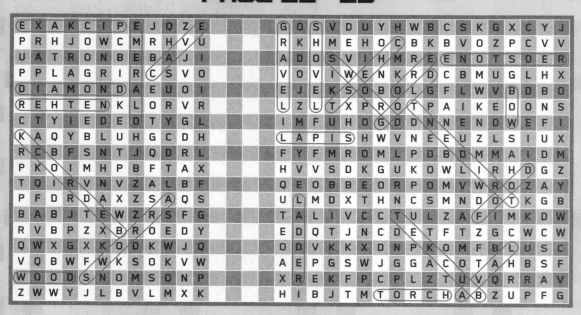

PAGE 25:

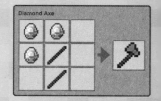
Diamond Axe

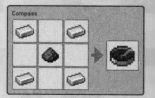
Compass

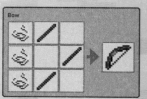
Bow

PAGE 26-27:

1. b 2. c 3. c 4. b
5. c 6. c 7. b 8. a
9. b 10. c

PAGE 34:

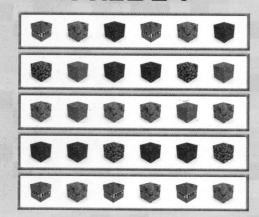

PAGE 35:

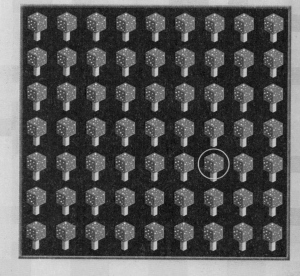

PAGE 44:

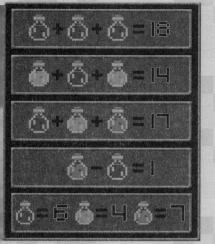

$$\text{potion} + \text{potion} + \text{potion} = 18$$
$$\text{potion} + \text{potion} + \text{potion} = 14$$
$$\text{potion} + \text{potion} + \text{potion} = 17$$
$$\text{potion} - \text{potion} = 1$$
$$\text{potion} = 6 \quad \text{potion} = 4 \quad \text{potion} = 7$$

PAGE 45:

Across/Down answers:
COAL, BLOCKS, CREEPER, GHAST, NETHER, SAND, REDSTONE, SANDBOX, MOJANG, BIOMES, STEVE

PAGE 51:

1
It is brown.
It can have a green top.
It can change colour depending on what biome it is in.
Answer: Grass block

2
It is a neutral mob.
It has unique teleportation abilities.
It has purple eyes.
Answer: An Enderman

3
It is a passive mob.
It can mumble.
It will run inside at night or during rain.
Answer: Villager

4
It spawns at a light level of 7 or less.
Spiders have a 1% chance to spawn with one of them riding it.
It is hostile.
Answer: Skeleton

5
It is a neutral mob.
It is found in the Nether.
It will attack you if you do not have at least one piece of golden armour.
Answer: Piglin

PAGE 46-47:

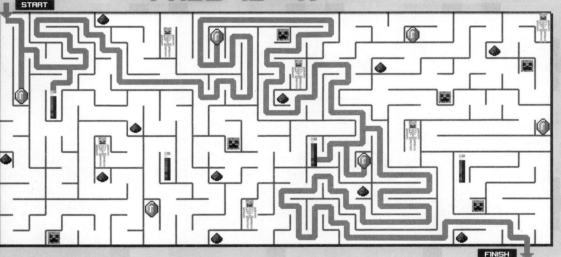

START

FINISH

PAGE 54:

PAGE 67:

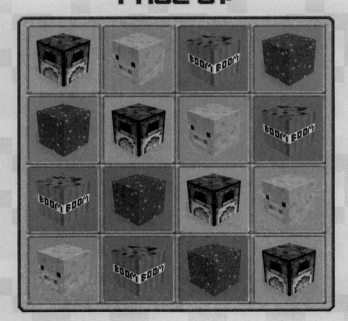

75

ANSWERS

PAGE 62-63:

1. ⊗ 2. ⊗ 3. ✓ 4. ⊗ 5. ✓
6. ✓ 7. ✓ 8. ⊗ 9. ⊗ 10. ✓
11. ✓ 12. ✓ 13. ⊗ 14. ✓ 15. ✓
16. ⊗ 17. ✓ 18. ⊗ 19. ✓ 20. ✓

PAGE 66:

PAGE 64-65:

PAGE 72-73:

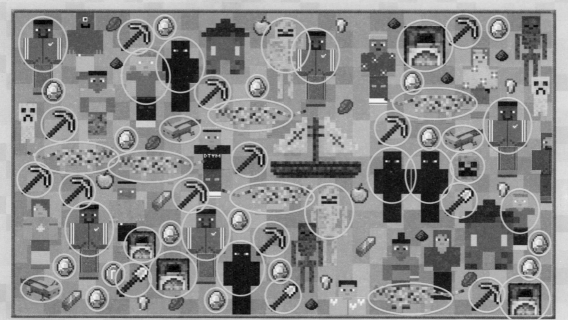

100% UNOFFICIAL
MINECRAFTERS UNITE

I ♥ MINECRAFT

▚ 100% UNOFFICIAL ▞
MINECRAFTERS UNITE

GAME OVER